THE COMPLETE PIANO PLAYER
HIT SONGS

Arranged by Kenneth Baker

Wise Publications
London/New York/Paris/Sydney/Copenhagen/Madrid/Tokyo

Exclusive Distributors:
Music Sales Limited
8/9 Frith Street,
London W1D 3JB,
England.
Music Sales Pty Limited
120 Rothschild Avenue,
Rosebery, NSW 2018,
Australia.

This book © Copyright 1992, 2000 by Wise Publications.
(Previously published as The Complete Piano Player Anthology)
Order No. AM967934
ISBN 0-7119-8553-7

Compiled by Peter Evans.
Music arranged by Kenneth Baker.
Music processed by Dakota Music Service.
Cover photograph (Ray Charles) courtesy of London Features International.

Your Guarantee of Quality
As publishers, we strive to produce every book to the
highest commercial standards.
This book has been carefully designed to minimise awkward page turns
and to make playing from it a real pleasure.
Particular care has been given to specifying acid-free, neutral-sized
paper made from pulps which have not been elemental chlorine bleached.
This pulp is from farmed sustainable forests and was produced with
special regard for the environment.
Throughout, the printing and binding have been planned to ensure a sturdy,
attractive publication which should give years of enjoyment.
If your copy fails to meet our high standards, please
inform us and we will gladly replace it.

Music Sales' complete catalogue describes thousands of titles and is
available in full colour sections by subject, direct from Music Sales Limited.
Please state your areas of interest and send a cheque/postal order for £1.50 for postage to:
Music Sales Limited, Newmarket Road, Bury St. Edmunds, Suffolk IP33 3YB.

www.musicsales.com

Printed in Malta.

MICHELLE

Words & Music by John Lennon & Paul McCartney

way, ___ I will say the on - ly words I know that you'll un - der - stand. Mich - elle, ma belle, sont les mots qui vont très bien en - semble, très bien en - semble. I will say the on - ly words I know that you'll un - der - stand, my Mich - elle.

MORNING OF MY LIFE (IN THE MORNING)

Words & Music by Barry Alan Gibb

SOMETIMES WHEN WE TOUCH

Words & Music by Dan Hill & Barry Mann

UNCHAINED MELODY

Music by Alex North. Words by Hy Zaret

INTERLUDE

PORTRAIT OF MY LOVE

Words by David West. Music by Cyril Ornadel

13

TOO YOUNG

Words by Sylvia Dee. Music by Sid Lippman

LAY, LADY, LAY

Words & Music by Bob Dylan

TRY A LITTLE TENDERNESS

Words & Music by Harry Woods, Jimmy Campbell & Reg Connelly

She may be wear-y, __ wo-men do get wear-y, __ wear-ing the same __ shab-by dress.

And when she's wear-y, __ try a lit-tle ten-der-

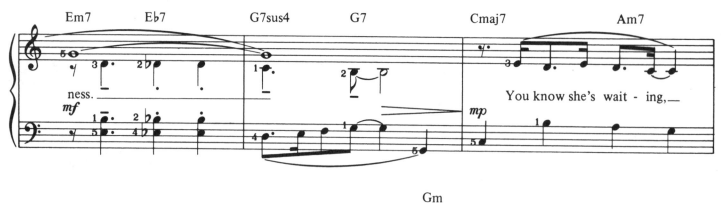

ness. __ You know she's wait-ing, __

just an-ti-ci-pa-ting __ things she may ne - ver pos-sess. __

While she's with-out them,— try a lit-tle ten-der - ness._____ It's

Poco rubato

not just sen-ti - men-tal, she has her grief and care._____ And a

word ——— that's soft and gen - tle,— makes it ea-si-er to bear.

With a lilt

You won't re-gret it,— wo-men don't for-get it,— love is their whole hap-pi - ness.—

It's all so ea - sy,— try a lit-tle ten-der - ness.

WONDERFUL TONIGHT

Words & Music by Eric Clapton

IF NOT FOR YOU

Words & Music by Bob Dylan

23

ALWAYS ON MY MIND

Words & Music by Wayne Thompson, Mark James & Johnny Christopher

TOO MUCH HEAVEN

Words & Music by Barry Gibb, Robin Gibb & Maurice Gibb

MORE THAN A WOMAN

Words & Music by Barry Gibb, Robin Gibb & Maurice Gibb

CHORUS

30

31

WE CAN WORK IT OUT

Words & Music by John Lennon & Paul McCartney

TICKET TO RIDE

Words & Music by John Lennon & Paul McCartney

she's got a tick-et to ride,___ but she don't care._____

cresc.

1. She
2. END OF SONG (FINE) I don't know why she's rid-ing so high,___

she ought to think twice and do right by me. Be-

fore she gets to say-ing good-bye,___ she ought to think twice, and do right by

me. She

D.S. al Fine

UPTOWN GIRL

Words & Music by Billy Joel

37

PIANO MAN

Words & Music by Billy Joel

INTERLUDE

39

DANIEL

Words & Music by Elton John & Bernie Taupin

41

MIDNIGHT IN MOSCOW

Based on a song by Vassili Soloviev and M. Matusovsky. New Musical arrangement by Kenny Ball

SATIN DOLL

Words by Johnny Mercer. Music by Duke Ellington & Billy Strayhorn

HONEYSUCKLE ROSE

Music by Thomas 'Fats' Waller. Words by Andy Razaf

MOONGLOW

Words & Music by Will Hudson, Eddie de Lange & Irving Mills

BLUESETTE

Words by Norman Gimbel. Music by Jean Thielemans

make your next Spring-time your gold wed – ding ring - time, so dry your eyes, don't you pout, don't you fret, good-y___ good times are com – ing, Blues – ette,___ Long as there's love in your heart to share, dear Blues – ette, don't des – pair.

52

YOUR SONG

Words & Music by Elton John and Bernie Taupin

55

NEW YORK STATE OF MIND

Words & Music by Billy Joel

57

THE LONGEST TIME

Words & Music by Billy Joel

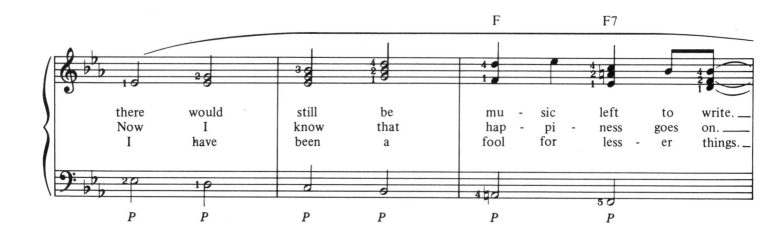

there would   still   be   mu - sic   left   to   write. __
Now   I   know   that   hap - pi - ness   goes   on. __
I   have   been   a   fool   for   less - er   things. __

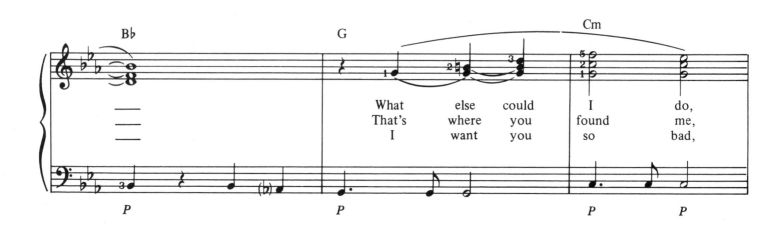

What   else   could   I   do,
That's   where   you   found   me,
I   want   you   so   bad,

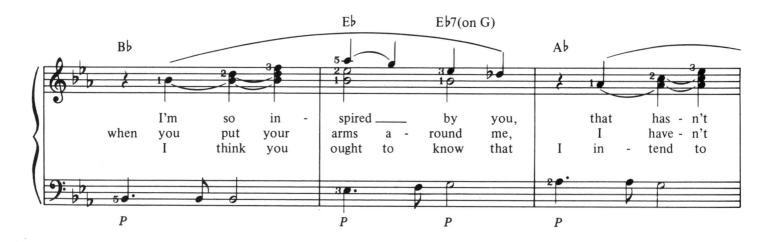

when   I'm   so   in - spired __ by   you,   that   has - n't
    you   put   your   arms   a - round   me,   I   have - n't
I   think   you   ought   to   know   that   I   in - tend   to

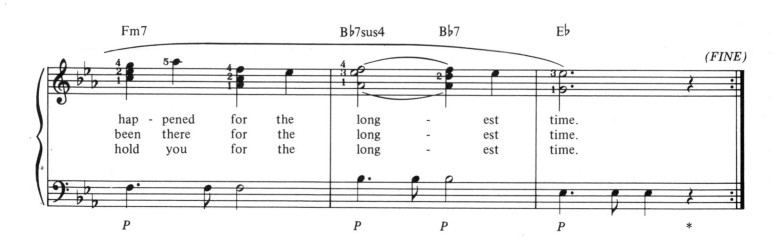

hap - pened   for   the   long - est   time.
been   there   for   the   long - est   time.
hold   you   for   the   long - est   time.

INTERLUDE

BUT NOT FOR ME

Music by George Gershwin

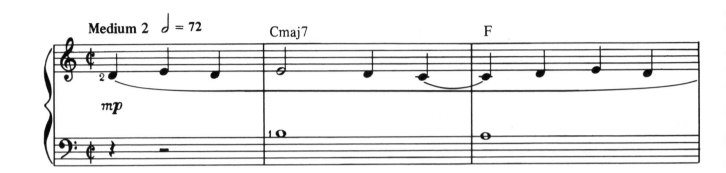

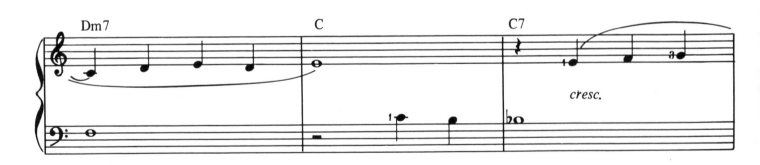

pass thumb under 3rd finger

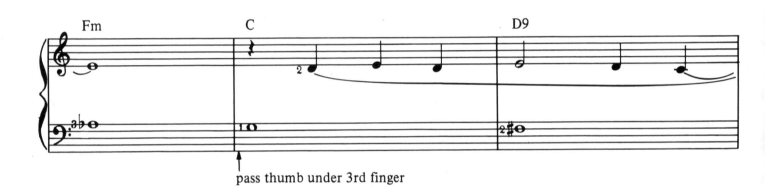

cross 2nd finger over 3rd

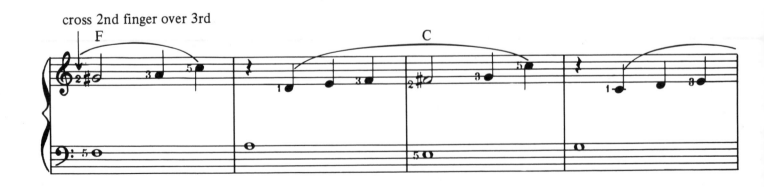

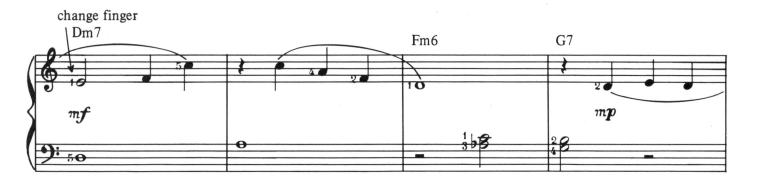

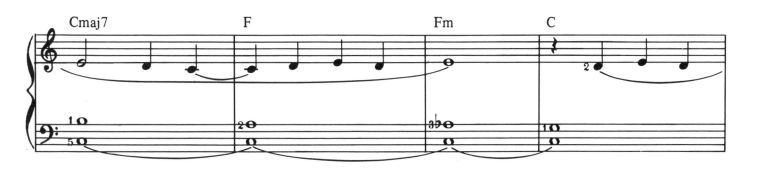

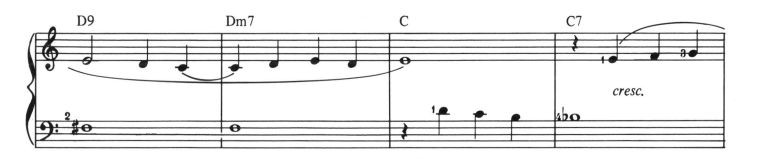

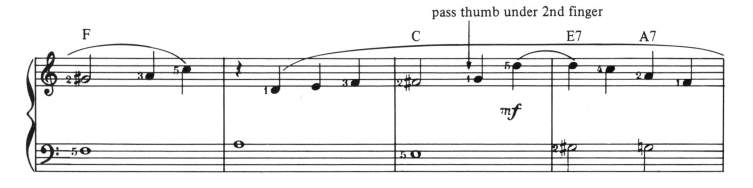

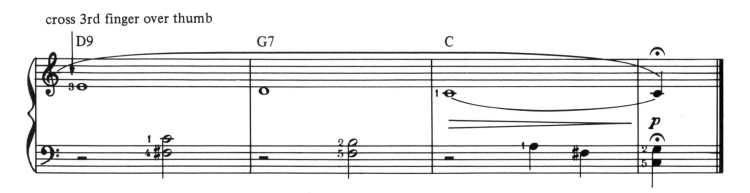

63

HAPPY XMAS (WAR IS OVER)

Words & Music by John Lennon & Yoko Ono

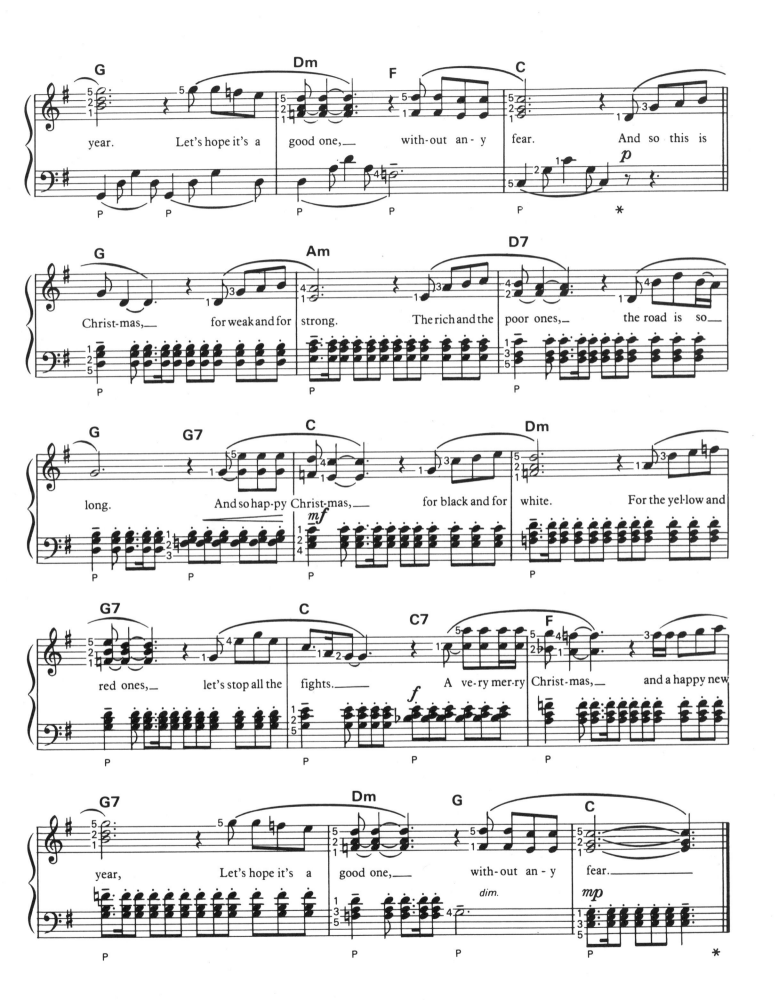

EVERYTHING IS BEAUTIFUL

Words & Music by Ray Stevens

BYE BYE LOVE

Words & Music by Felice & Boudleaux Bryant

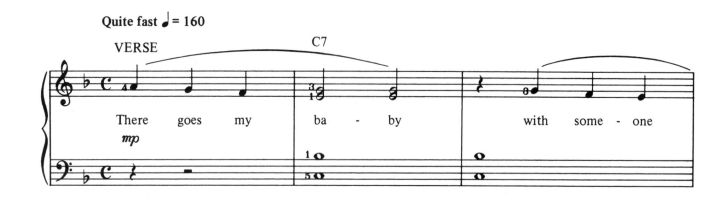

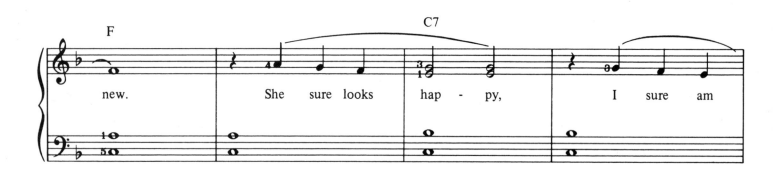

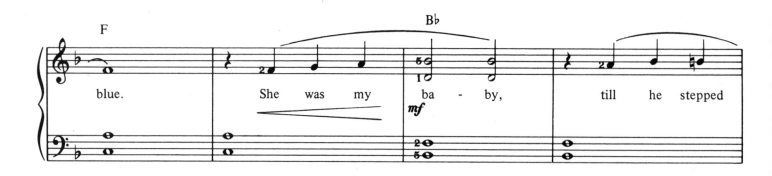

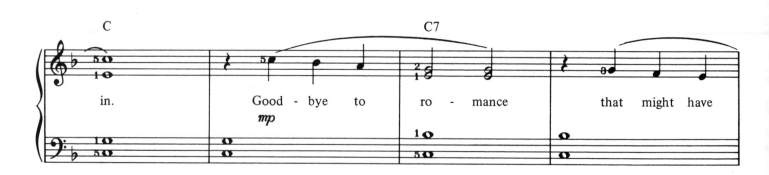

CHORUS

RELEASE ME

Words & Music by Eddie Miller, Dub Williams, Robert Yount & Robert Harris

lease me and let me love a - gain.

I have found a new love dear, _____ and

I will al - ways want you near. _____ Her

lips are warm, while yours are cold, _____ re -

lease me, my dar - ling, let me go. _____

YOUR CHEATIN' HEART

Words & Music by Hank Williams

FUNNY HOW TIME SLIPS AWAY

Words & Music by Willie Nelson

I CAN'T STOP LOVING YOU

Words & Music by Don Gibson

HEY JUDE

Words & Music by John Lennon & Paul McCartney

78

HERE, THERE AND EVERYWHERE

Words & Music by John Lennon & Paul McCartney

MEMORIES ARE MADE OF THIS

Words & Music by Terry Gilkyson, Richard Dehr & Frank Miller

ON A SLOW BOAT TO CHINA

Words & Music by Frank Loesser

EASTENDERS

Composed by Leslie Osborne & Simon May

GOING HOME

Composed by Mark Knopfler

Rubato. With expression

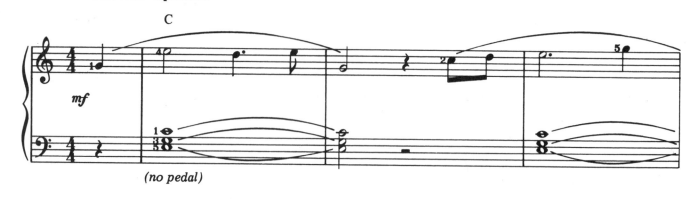

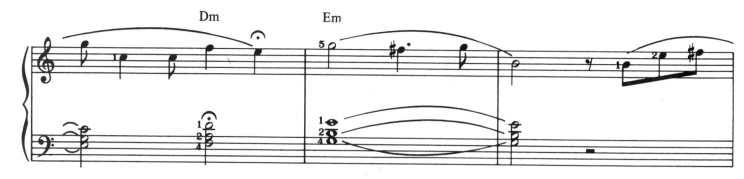

Medium tempo ♩ = 88

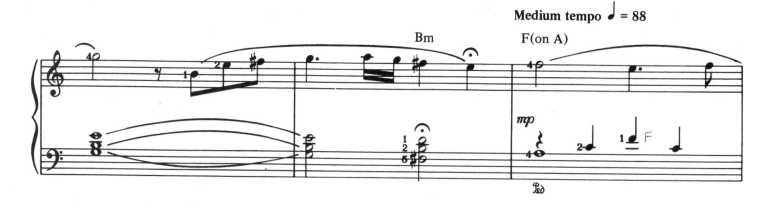

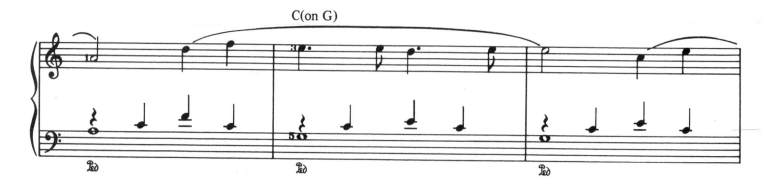

ANGELA (THEME FROM TAXI)

Composed by Bob James

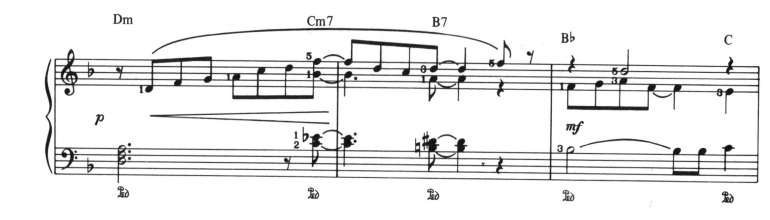

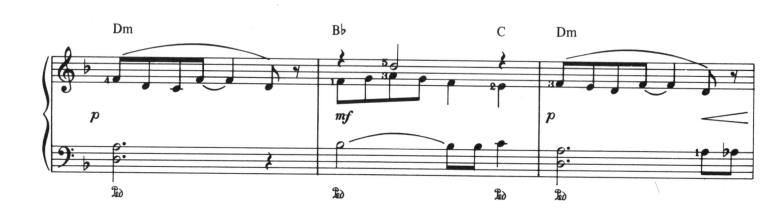

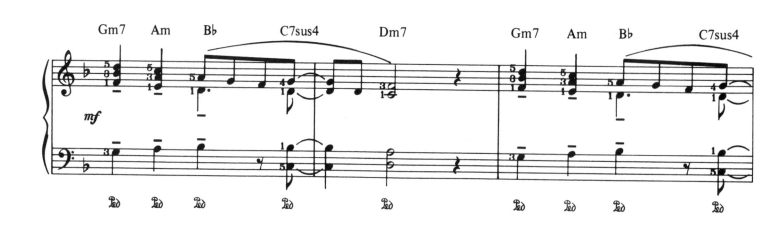

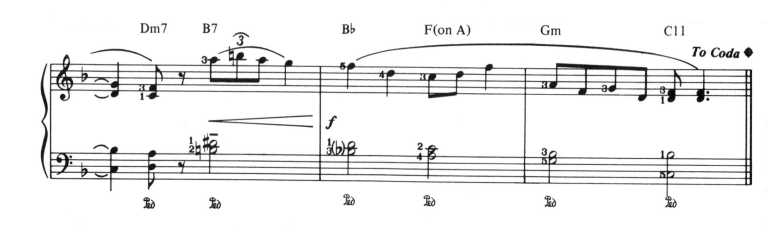

TILL THERE WAS YOU

Words & Music by Meredith Willson

2/04 (50128)